The Complete Story of the
Three Blind Mice

by John W. Ivimey

Illustrated by Paul Galdone

A TRUMPET CLUB SPECIAL EDITION

Published by The Trumpet Club
1540 Broadway, New York, New York 10036

Illustrations copyright © 1987 by the Estate of Paul Galdone

ISBN: 0-440-84315-4

This edition published by arrangement with Clarion Books/
Houghton Mifflin Company
Printed in the United States of America
September 1990

10 9 8 7 6 5 4 3
UPC

Three small mice

Three small mice
Wished for some fun
Wished for some fun

They made up their minds
to set out to roam,
Said they,
"'Tis dull to remain at home,"

And all the luggage they took was a comb,
These three small mice.

Three bold mice
Three bold mice
      Came to an inn
      Came to an inn
"Good evening host,
can you give us a bed?"

But the host just grinned and shook his head,

So they all slept out in the field instead,
These three bold mice.

Three cold mice
Three cold mice
    Woke up next morn
    Woke up next morn

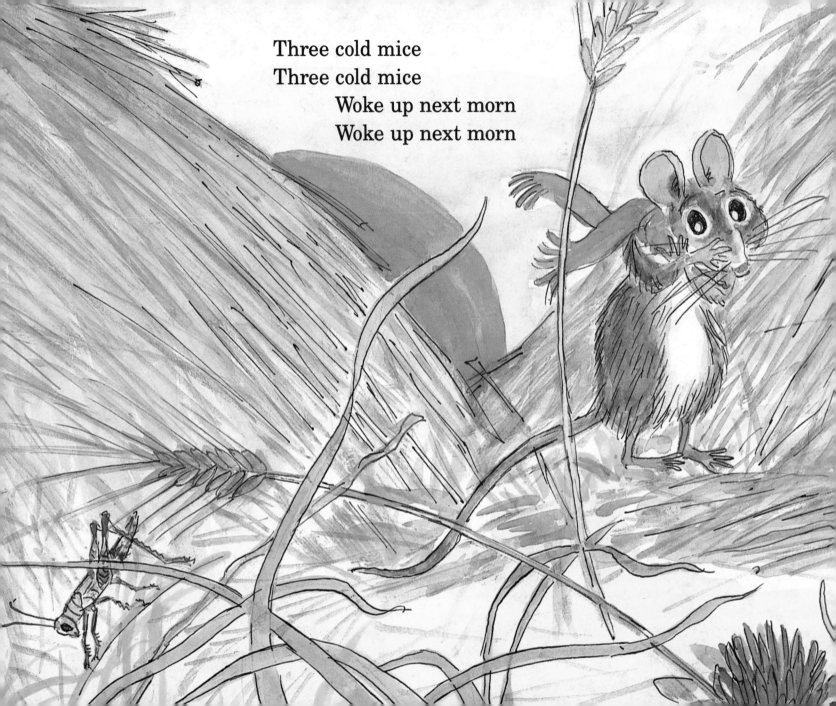

They each had a cold and a swollen face,
From sleeping all night in an open space,

So they rose quite early and left the place,
These three cold mice.

Three hungry mice
Three hungry mice
Searched for some food
Searched for some food

But all they found was a walnut shell
That lay by the side of a dried-up well.
Who had eaten the nut they could not tell,
These three hungry mice.

Three starved mice
Three starved mice
Came to a farm
Came to a farm

The farmer was eating some bread and cheese,
So they all went down on their hands and knees,

And squeaked, "Oh give us a morsel please,"
These three starved mice.

Three glad mice
Three glad mice
        Ate all they could
        Ate all they could

They felt so happy they danced with glee,
But the farmer's wife came in to see
What might this merry-making be,
Of three glad mice.
        Three poor mice
        Three poor mice
                Soon changed their tone
                Soon changed their tone

The farmer's wife said, "What are you at?
And why are you prancing around like that?

Just you wait,
I'll fetch the cat.
You naughty,
naughty mice."

Three scared mice
Three scared mice
    Ran for their lives
    Ran for their lives

The mention of "Cat" set their teeth on edge,
So they jumped out onto the window ledge,

And made a leap for the bramble hedge,
These three scared mice.

Three sad mice
Three sad mice
What could they do
What could they do

The bramble hedge was most unkind,
It scratched their eyes and made them blind,

Their way back home they could not find,
These three sad mice.

Three blind mice
Three blind mice
    See how they run
    See how they run
They all ran after the farmer's wife,
Who cut off their tails with a carving knife,

Did you ever see such a sight in your life,
As three blind mice?

Three sick mice
Three sick mice
        Gave way to tears
        Gave way to tears
They could not see, and they had no end,
They hoped for magic, then found a friend,
He gave them some "Never Too Late To Mend,"
These three sick mice.

Three wise mice
Three wise mice
      Rubbed rubbed away
      Rubbed rubbed away

DR. HARE'S
Magic Salve

And soon their tails began to grow,
And their eyes recovered their sight, you know,

They looked in the pond and it told them so,

These three wise mice.

Three happy mice
Three happy mice
    Soon settled down
    Soon settled down

They built a house,
so I hear tell,
Each learned a trade
and is doing well,

If you call upon them, ring the bell,
Three times twice.

Adaptation

Steve Parker

Heinemann Library
Chicago, Illinois

Customer Service 888-454-2279

Visit our website at www.heinemannlibrary.com

Designed by Celia Floyd
Originated by Dot Gradations
Printed in China by WKT

05

10 9 8 7 6 5 4 3

Library of Congress Cataloging-in-Publication Data
Parker, Steve, 1961-
    Adaptation / Steve Parker.
        p. cm. -- (Life processes)
    Includes bibliographical references (p.).
    ISBN 1-57572-335-2 (HC), 1-4034-4071-9 (Pbk.)
    1. Adaptation (Biology)--Juvenile literature. [1. Adaptation (Biology)] I. Title.

QH546 .G36 2000
578.4--dc21

00-040937

Acknowledgments
The author and publishers are grateful to the following for permission to reproduce copyright material: Bruce Coleman Collection/Mary Plage, p. 14; Corbis/Daniel Samuel Robbins, p. 9; NHPA, p. 20; NHPA/B & C Alexander, p. 22; NHPA/A.N.T., pp. 7, 24; NHPA/Anthony Bannister, p. 11, 25; NHPA/N. A. Callow, p. 4; NHPA/G. J. Cambridge, p. 18; NHPA/Vincente Gardia Canseco, p. 29; NHPA/Stephen Dalton, pp. 10, 16, 28; NHPA/Martin Harvey, pp. 12, 15; NHPA/Daniel Heuclin, p. 25; NHPA/David Hosking, p. 27; NHPA/E. A. Janes, p. 19; NHPA/Darek Karp, p. 8; NHPA/David Middleton, p. 4; NHPA/Dr. Eckart Pott, p. 13; NHPA/John Shaw, p. 23; NHPA/Hellio & Van Ingen, p. 17; NHPA/Roy Waller, p. 19; NHPA/Norbert Wu, p. 21; Oxford Scientific Films/ Daniel J. Cox, p. 4; Oxford Scientific Films/Michael Fogden, p. 10; Oxford Scientific Films/Richard Herrmann, p. 20; Oxford Scientific Films/Roland Mayr, p. 26; Oxford Scientific Films/Colin Milkins, p. 6; Oxford Scientific Films/Sean Morris, p. 27.

Cover photograph reproduced with permission of Tony Stone.

Every effort has been made to contact copyright holders of any material reproduced in this book. Any omissions will be rectified in subsequent printings if notice is given to the publisher.

Some words are shown in bold, **like this.** You can find out what they mean by looking in the glossary.